BASIC PNEUMATICS

LEARNING ACTIVITY PACKET

BASIC PNEUMATIC CIRCUITS

BB834-BA02XEN

BASIC PNEUMATIC CIRCUITS

INTRODUCTION

This LAP will discuss two new types of actuators: single-acting cylinders and motors. Both of these actuators are often used in pneumatic circuits.

The last segment of this LAP will strengthen the ability to interpret and create pneumatic schematics. These are important skills to have when working with fluid power.

ITEMS NEEDED

Amatrol Supplied

    1   85-BP Basic Pneumatic Learning System

    1   85-IP Intermediate Pneumatic Learning System (optional)

School Supplied

    1   Compressed Air Supply

    1   Adjustable Wrench

TABLE OF CONTENTS

SEGMENT 1

SINGLE-ACTING CYLINDER CIRCUITS

OBJECTIVE 1 DESCRIBE THE FUNCTION OF A SINGLE-ACTING PNEUMATIC CYLINDER AND GIVE AN APPLICATION

Single-acting pneumatic cylinders are powered by compressed air in one direction only. To move in the other direction (return), another force is used, such as gravity of the load or a spring. These cylinders are used in applications where the load will cause it to return or, if the load is light enough, a spring can be used to return the rod.

An example of a spring-return cylinder application is the pneumatic robot gripper shown in figure 1. Pressure is needed in order to create a force to clamp. But the force to unclamp the part is so little, a spring inside the cylinder can be used.

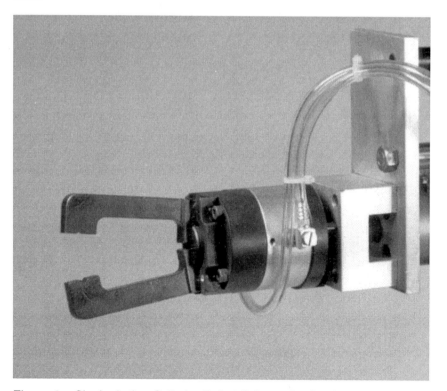

Figure 1.   Single-Acting Cylinder Robot Gripper Application

A single-acting, spring-return cylinder, shown in figure 2, is a type of cylinder that consists of a piston/rod assembly that moves inside a barrel-shaped body, a single port for air to enter and leave, and a spring to return the rod assembly to its de-energized position.

Single-acting cylinders can be made to power in either direction. When they are powered to extend, as shown in figure 2, they are called "single-acting to extend" cylinders. When they are powered to retract, they are called "single-acting to retract" cylinders.

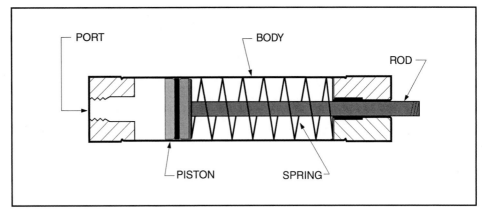

Figure 2.   Basic Construction of a Single-Acting, Spring Return Cylinder

The schematic symbols for the single-acting, spring-return cylinders are shown in figure 3.

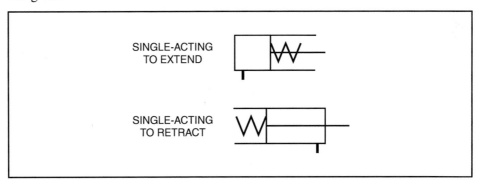

Figure 3.   Schematic Symbols for the Single-Acting, Spring-Return Cylinders

Activity 1. Basic Operation of a Single-Acting, Spring-Return Cylinder

Procedure Overview

In this procedure, you will connect and cycle a single-acting cylinder. This will demonstrate the basic operation of the cylinder.

❑ 1. Before connecting your cylinder circuit, perform the following substeps.

A. Close the shutoff valve if not already closed.

B. Adjust the regulator to minimum by pulling up on the knob to unlock it and then turning the knob counterclockwise (CCW) fully.

C. If not already attached, connect the compressed air supply source to the supply connection located on the pneumatic instrumentation module.

❑ 2. Set up the circuit shown in figure 4. In this circuit, the supply manifold is connected directly to the cylinder.

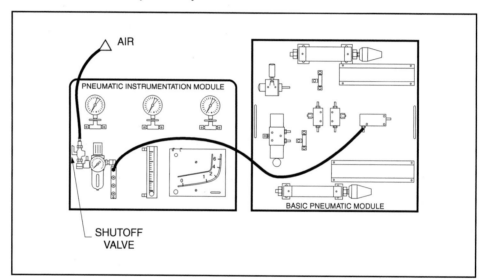

Figure 4.   Pictorial of a Circuit to Extend a Single-Acting, Spring-Return Cylinder

❑ 3. Open the shutoff valve.

You are now ready to extend the cylinder.

❑ 4. Lift the knob of the regulator and turn it slowly CW until the cylinder extends fully.

You should observe that the cylinder starts to extend at low pressure, as shown in figure 5. More pressure is needed to completely extend the cylinder because the spring is being compressed further.

The supply pressure must provide enough force to overcome the load and compress the spring. The air on the backside of the piston is allowed to freely escape through openings in the rod end.

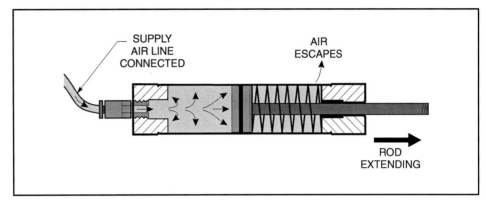

Figure 5.   Single-Acting, Spring Return Cylinder Extending

❑ 5. Retract the cylinder completely by slowly turning the regulator knob CCW, reducing the regulator setting to minimum.

You should observe that the spring slowly retracts the cylinder rod as the regulator bleeds the air from the cylinder, as shown in figure 6.

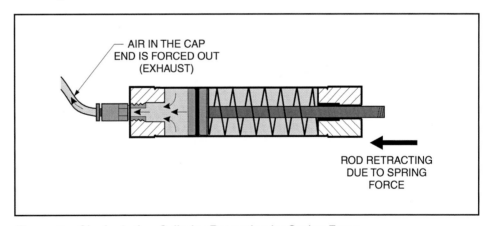

Figure 6.   Single-Acting Cylinder Retracting by Spring Force

As with double-acting cylinders, single-acting cylinders also have piston seals, rod seals, and a rod bushing.

❑ 6. Repeat steps 4 and 5 several times to become more familiar with the operation of the single-acting, spring-return cylinder.

❑ 7. Close the shutoff valve.

❑ 8. Disconnect the hoses and store them.

Instead of using a pressure regulator to operate a single-acting cylinder, a 3-way directional control valve is normally used. The 3-way, 2-position (also called 3/2) DCV, shown in figure 7, is simpler than the 4-way DCV because it has one less flow path and no center position. It is designed to take advantage of the fact that a single-acting cylinder does not need an air supply to return the rod.

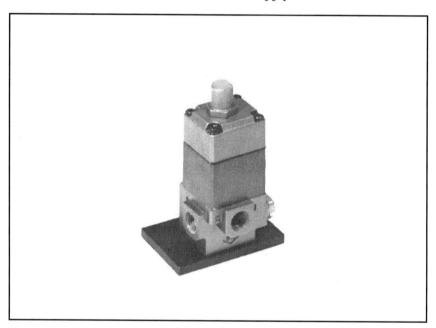

Figure 7.   A Pneumatic 3-Way Directional Control Valve

The 3-way DCV allows the machine operator to power the cylinder in one direction and exhaust the air to return the cylinder. This valve is used in any application where the actuator needs to be powered in one direction only.

The 3/2 DCV is manufactured in two types: N.C. (normally closed) and N.O. (normally open). Some 3/2 DCVs can be connected to provide either function.

A typical N.C. application is in a cylinder clamping circuit where unclamping does not need pneumatic power and can easily be done with a spring. N.O. types are used in safety circuits to hold, lock, or brake a machine in position pneumatically in the event that operator power is lost.

The 3-way DCV, as shown in figure 8, consists of the same four major components used in 4 or 5-way DCVs.

A movable spool slides back and forth inside a body to change the flow path connections between ports. A spring keeps the spool shifted to one end where it is de-energized. An operator of some type shifts the spool to energize it.

The only difference from a 4 or 5-way valve is a 3-way valve only has 3 ports: Port A is the actuator port, Port P is the supply port, and Port E is the exhaust port.

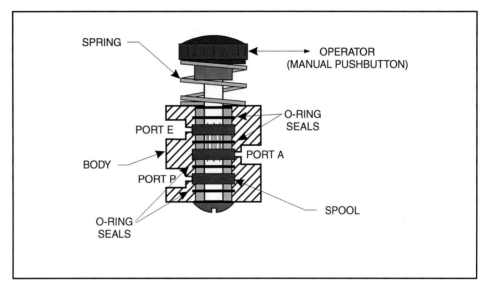

Figure 8.   Basic Construction of a Manually-Operated 3-Way DCV

The schematic symbol for a 3-way, 2-position (3/2) manually- operated pneumatic valve is shown in figure 9. The same guidelines used for reading 5-way schematic symbols apply to 3-way schematic symbols. In this case, the valve connects port A to port E in the normal position (spring in control). When the manual operator (pushbutton) is pressed, Port P is connected to Port A allowing air to flow to the actuator.

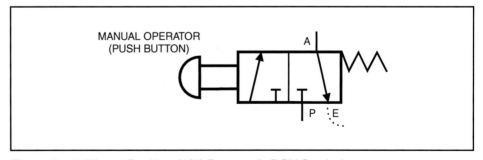

Figure 9.   3-Way, 2-Position (3/2) Pneumatic DCV Symbol

The parts identified on the 3/2 DCVs shown in figures 8 and 9 indicate that these values were manufactured as N.C. types. However, they can also be used to provide a N.O. function by connecting the supply to Port E, the actuator to Port A, and the exhaust to Port P.

SKILL 1	CONNECT AND OPERATE A SINGLE-ACTING PNEUMATIC CYLINDER USING A 3/2 MANUALLY-OPERATED DCV

Procedure Overview

In this procedure, you will set up a basic pneumatic circuit that will allow you to reciprocate a single-acting, spring-return cylinder using a 3-way directional control valve.

❑ 1. Locate the model 85-IP Intermediate Pneumatic Module, shown in figure 10, and place it next to the 85-BP Basic Pneumatic Modules, as shown in figure 11.

NOTE

Just read this procedure if you do not have the Amatrol 85-IP Intermediate Pneumatic module shown in figure 10. This skill uses a 3-way valve that is supplied with the 85-IP module.

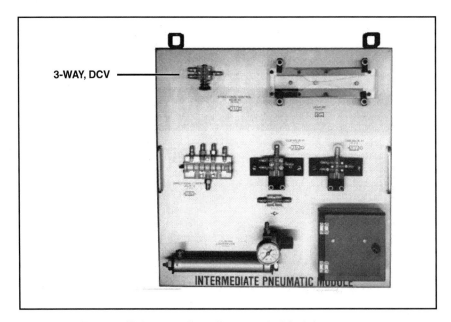

Figure 10. The 85-IP Intermediate Pneumatic Module

❑ 2. Set up the circuit shown in figures 11 and 12.

The 3-way DCV is located on the 85-IP Intermediate Pneumatic Module. Gauge C will indicate the pressure in the cylinder line.

In this circuit the 3/2 DCV is connected to provide a N.C. function.

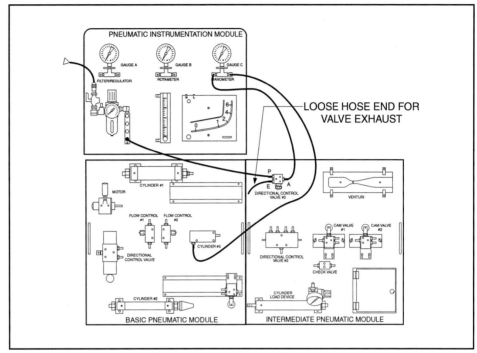

Figure 11. Pictorial of a Single-Acting Cylinder Circuit

CAUTION

To open the DCV's exhaust port (E port), you must connect one end of a hose to this port. When you perform this procedure, tie or hold down the loose end of this hose to avoid whipping and possible injury.

NOTE

Normally, for this application, the E-port does not have a fitting and exhausts directly to atmosphere. However, later you will use this valve in a different application where you will need to connect the supply to this port. This is why it has a fitting.

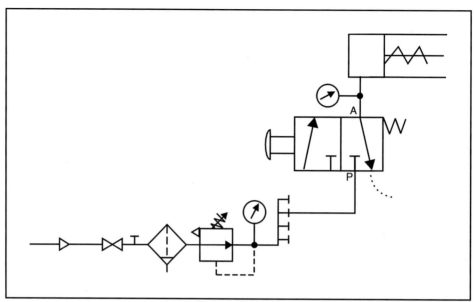

Figure 12. Schematic of a N.C. Single-Acting Cylinder Circuit

❑ 3. Connect the compressed air supply source to the male quick-connect plug on the instrumentation module and open the shutoff valve.

❑ 4. Turn the regulator adjustment CW until the pressure at the regulator gauge reads 40 psi/276 kPa.

Compressed air is now at Port P of the DCV. Gauge C should read 0 psi/0 kPa.

Figure 13 shows the condition of the 3-way DCV and the single-acting, spring-return cylinder at this time. The manual operator (push button) is not pressed. The valve is said to be in the normal or de-energized position. In this position, supply pressure is blocked and the cylinder port is open to atmosphere through the exhaust port of the DCV. The cylinder spring holds the rod retracted. This is also shown in the schematic of figure 14.

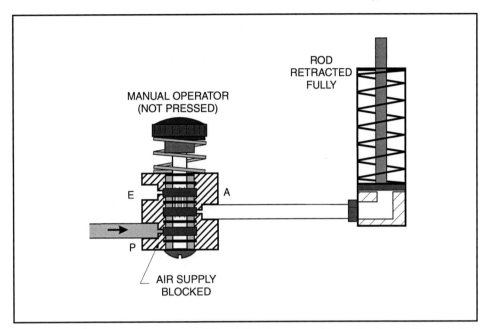

Figure 13. Manually-Operated, 3-Way DCV Connected to a Single- Acting, Spring Return Cylinder

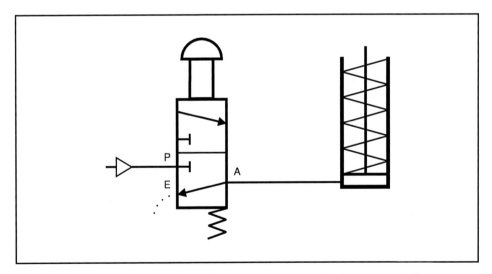

Figure 14. Schematic of 3-Way DCV Connected to a Single-Acting Cylinder

❑ 5. Now test your pneumatic circuit by pressing in on the manual operator to extend the cylinder rod. Continue to hold the button in.

When the manual operator is pressed, air flows through the valve from Port P to Port A, as shown in figures 15 and 16. From Port A, the air enters the cap end of the cylinder and causes it to extend.

As the cylinder extends, the spring compresses but its force is much less than the compressed air so it has no effect. The air on the rod side rushes out through a small air hole.

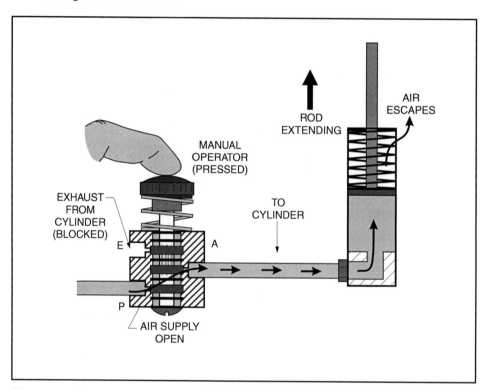

Figure 15. Manually-Operated 3-Way DCV in the Energized Position

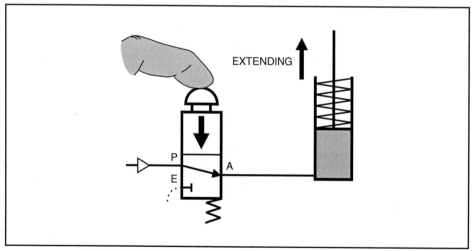

Figure 16. 3-Way DCV in Energized Position

❑ 6. Release the manual operator.

In figure 17, you should observe that the cylinder retracts. When the valve shifts to its de-energized condition, Port P is blocked and Port A is connected to Port E. This causes the pressure on the cap end of the cylinder to drop to zero. The spring force can now retract the cylinder. As it does, the air in the cap end is pushed out of the exhaust port into atmosphere.

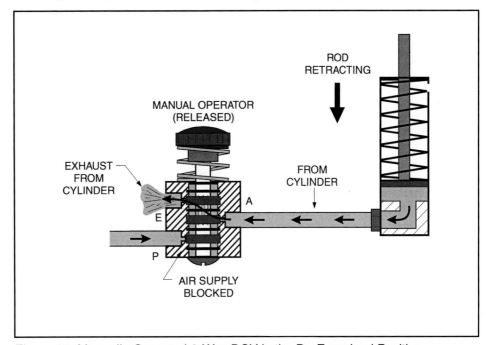

Figure 17. Manually-Operated 3-Way DCV in the De-Energized Position

❑ 7. Repeat steps 5 and 6 several times to cycle the cylinder. During one of the cycles, release the button while the cylinder rod is extending and is in mid-stroke. What happens? Does the cylinder stop, keep extending, or retract?

_____

_____

You should observe that the cylinder retracts because the DCV returns to the de-energized position, blocking pressure and exhausting the cylinder.

❑ 8. Turn the regulator adjustment CCW fully to reduce the pressure to a minimum.

❑ 9. Close the shutoff valve.

❑10. Now switch the hose ends at the DCV, as shown in figure 18. In this circuit, the 3-way DCV is connected to provide the N.O. function.

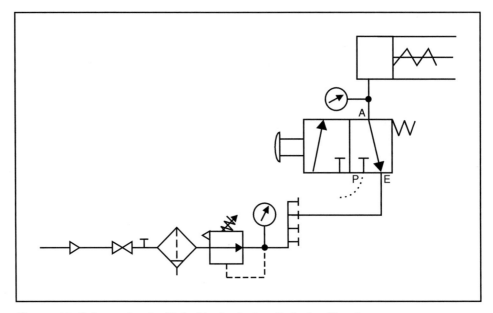

Figure 18. Schematic of a N.O. Single-Acting Cylinder Circuit

CAUTION

To exhaust through the DCV, you must connect one end of a hose to Port P. When you perform this procedure, tie or hold down the loose end of this hose to avoid whipping and possible injury.

❑11. Open the shutoff valve.

❑12. Turn the regulator adjustment CW until pressure at the regulator gauge reads 40 psi/276 kPa.

The single-acting, spring-return cylinder should extend fully as regulator pressure is increased to 40 psi/276 kPa because the 3/2 DCV is providing a N.O. condition. Supply flows through the DCV directly to the cylinder.

☐ 13. Press and hold in the pushbutton of the 3/2 DCV. When the manual operator is pressed, supply air is blocked and the cylinder is exhausted through Port P, as shown in figure 19, causing the cylinder to retract.

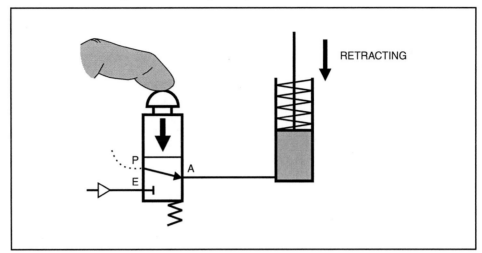

Figure 19. 3-Way, N.O. DCV in Energized Position

☐ 14. Release the manual operator.

You should observe that the cylinder extends. When the valve shifts to its de-energized condition, supply air is reconnected to Port A and the exhaust is blocked, as shown in figure 18.

☐ 15. Repeat steps 13 and 14 several times to cycle the cylinder to become more familiar with a 3-way N.O. circuit.

☐ 16. Turn the regulator adjustment CCW fully to reduce pressure to a minimum.

The cylinder should retract as the pressure is decreased.

☐ 17. Close the shutoff valve.

☐ 18. Disconnect and store the hoses.

1. The pneumatic 3-way DCV has _____ ports.

2. The part of the 3-way DCV that changes the flow path is called the _____.

3. A single-acting _____ cylinder consists of a piston/rod assembly, a single port, and a spring.

4. Single-acting cylinders are returned by springs or the _____.

5. A(n) _____ DCV is used when an actuator needs to be powered in one direction only.

SEGMENT 2

BASIC MOTOR CIRCUITS

OBJECTIVE 5	DESCRIBE THE FUNCTION OF A PNEUMATIC MOTOR AND GIVE AN APPLICATION

The pneumatic motor is an actuator that converts compressed air flow into rotary motion. It is used in applications where low force rotary output is needed. Examples include pneumatic drills, mixing motors, and small winches.

Figure 20. Typical Air Motor

Pneumatic motors operate by using air pressure to create a turning force called torque at the motor shaft. Once the resisting torque of the load at the motor shaft is overcome, the shaft starts to rotate. Any additional air pressure beyond that needed to start the rotation determines the speed (rpm) of the motor. See figure 21.

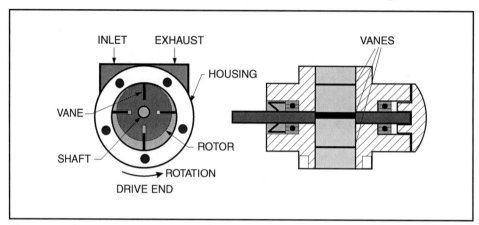

Figure 21. Construction of a Typical Air Motor

Most pneumatic motors are made to turn in one direction only. These are called uni-directional. Pneumatic motors that rotate in either direction are also available, and are called bi-directional. The schematic symbols for each type are shown in figure 22.

Notice in figure 22 that the arrows (triangles) are hollow. This indicates that the medium is a gas. Also, the arrows point inward to indicate that flow goes into the motor.

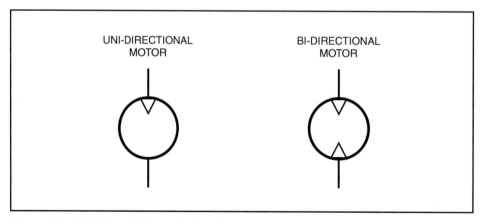

Figure 22. Air Motor Schematic Symbols

Procedure Overview

In this procedure, you will set up a basic pneumatic circuit that will allow you to operate a motor. The circuit uses a 3-way DCV to control the uni-directional motor.

❏ 1. Set up the pneumatic motor circuit shown in figures 23 and 24.

NOTE

Just read this procedure if you do not have the Amatrol 85-IP Intermediate Pneumatic Module. This skill uses a 3-way valve that is supplied with the 85-IP Module.

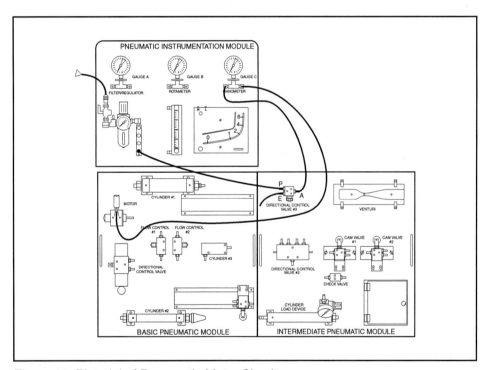

Figure 23. Pictorial of Pneumatic Motor Circuit

CAUTION

To open the DCV E-port, you must connect one end of a hose to this port. While performing this procedure, tie or hold down the loose end of this hose to avoid whipping and possible injury.

Examine the schematic shown in figure 24. Compare it to the pictorial of figure 23.

NOTE

The pictorial and schematic include a muffler which is attached to the air motor. Operation of the muffler will be covered in the next objective.

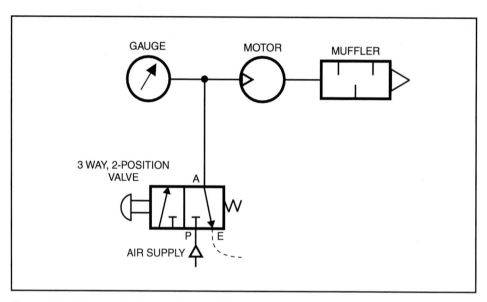

Figure 24. Pneumatic Motor Schematic

❑ 2. Perform the following substeps to connect the compressed air supply.

    A. If not already connected, connect the compressed air supply source to the male quick-connect on the instrumentation module.

    B. Open the shutoff valve.

❑ 3. Turn the regulator adjustment CW until the pressure at the regulator gauge reads 30 psi/207 kPa.

Compressed air is now at Port P of the DCV. Gauge C should read 0 psi/0 kPa.

❑ 4. Test your circuit by pressing in on the manual operator to run the motor. Continue to hold the button in. If the motor hasn't been run in a while, you may have to help it start by spinning the shaft.

You should observe that the motor runs slowly.

Also listen to the noise level as air is exhausted through the muffler.

❑ 5. Record the pressure at Gauge C.

Gauge C _____ (psi/kPa)

Gauge C pressure should be less than 20 psi/138 kPa because there is no load on the motor.

❑ 6. Release the DCV manual operator to block flow to the motor.

You should observe that the motor stops quickly. Also you should observe that the pressure at Gauge C drops to 0 psi/0 kPa because the motor inlet is open to the atmosphere.

❑ 7. Repeat steps 4 and 6 several times to become more familiar with the operation of the air motor.

❑ 8. To observe the effect that pressure has on motor operation, adjust the regulator CW until the pressure at the regulator gauge reads 50 psi / 345 kPa.

❑ 9. Press in the manual operator of the DCV.

You should observe that motor speed and noise level have increased along with the pressure at Gauge C.

❑ 10. Record the pressure at Gauge C.

Gauge C _____ (psi/kPa)

Gauge C pressure should be higher than it was in step 5. This shows that an increase in pressure will cause an air motor to increase speed.

❑ 11. Release the DCV manual operator to stop the motor.

❑ 12. Turn the regulator adjustment CCW fully to reduce the pressure to a minimum.

❑ 13. Close the shutoff valve.

❑ 14. Disconnect and store the hoses.

Exhausting air from pneumatic components can create a very loud noise. This is especially noticeable with high-speed air motors, which are considerably louder than electrical and hydraulic motors.

To reduce this noise, mufflers, sometimes called silencers, are placed in the exhaust port of the component. Mufflers reduce the noise levels in the same manner as the muffler does in an automobile.

The motor used on the Amatrol trainer is equipped with a muffler, as shown in figure 25. If the motor must run in both directions, mufflers are mounted at the exhaust ports of the DCV instead of at the motor's exhaust port.

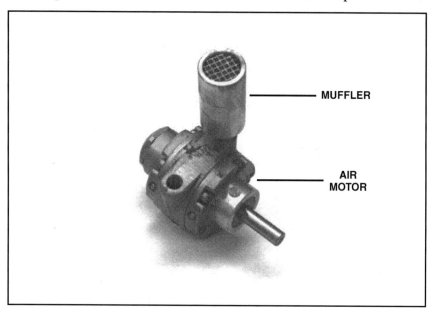

Figure 25. An Air Motor Equipped with Muffler

The schematic symbol for a muffler is shown in figure 26.

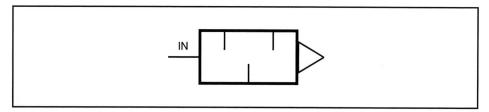

Figure 26. Air Muffler Schematic Symbol

Activity 2. Air Muffler Operation

Procedure Overview

In this procedure, you will demonstrate the operation of the air motor without the air muffler.

❑ 1. Set up the pneumatic motor circuit shown in figure 27.

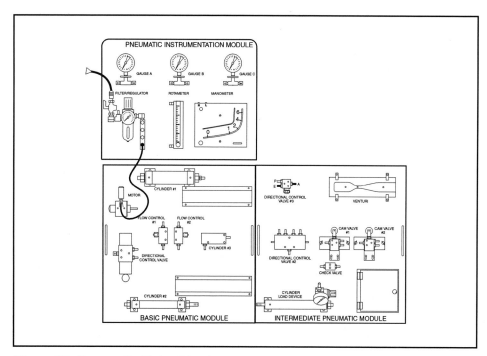

Figure 27. Pneumatic Motor Circuit

❑ 2. If not already connected, connect the compressed air supply source to the male quick-connect on the instrumentation module and open the shutoff valve.

❑ 3. Slowly increase the regulator pressure to 30 psi / 207 kPa. As you do this, listen to the sound of the motor with the muffler attached. The sound is much quieter than it would be without the muffler.

❑ 4. Decrease the regulator setting to its minimum setting to stop the motor.

❑ 5. Now remove the muffler from the air motor by twisting it CCW with your hand. Use a pair of pliers if needed.

❑ 6. Now increase the regulator pressure to 30 psi / 207 kPa and listen to the motor.

You should notice that it is much louder. This shows why a muffler is an important component.

❑ 7. Reduce the regulator pressure to minimum and close the shutoff valve.

❑ 8. Reattach the muffler.

❑ 9. Disconnect the hoses and store them.

There are three common commercially available designs of pneumatic motors:
- Vane/Rotor
- Axial Piston
- Radial Piston

Vane/Rotor

The standard vane-type motor, shown in figure 28, is the one furnished with the Amatrol trainer and has four vanes. Motors with more vanes are available if smoother rotation is required.

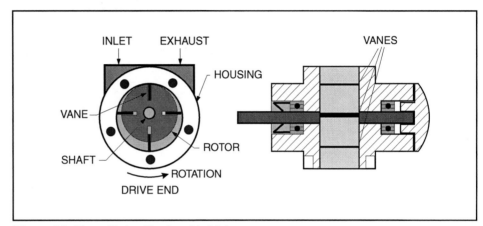

Figure 28. Vane-Rotor Design Air Motor

The vane-rotor air motor is the most common type found in industrial plants. They are used to drive conveyors, pumps, and blowers, especially in hazardous or explosive atmospheres. Portable hand tools, as shown in figure 29, also use this design.

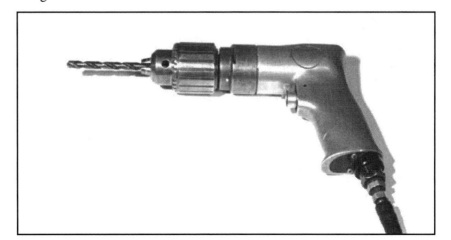

Figure 29. Portable Hand Air Tool

Axial Piston

The axial piston motor, shown in figure 30, has high starting torque. This type of motor is popular in the construction industry for use in hoists, winches, and air tools.

However, this motor is manufactured only in small sizes; 3-1/2 horsepower or less.

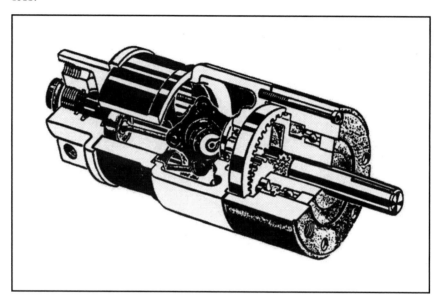

Figure 30. An Axial Piston Air Motor

Radial Piston

Radial piston air motors have the same characteristics as the axial piston type and are used in the same types of applications. Figure 31 shows a radial piston air motor.

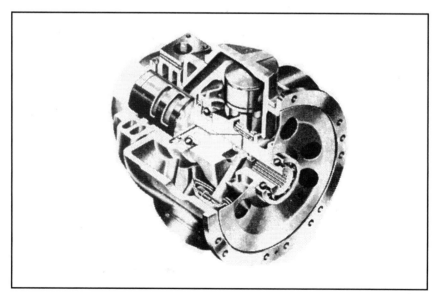

Figure 31. A Radial Piston Air Motor

1. The pneumatic motor converts fluid power to _____ motion.

2. To reduce the noise level from air motors, _____ are used in the exhaust.

3. The _____ piston air motor has a high starting torque.

4. The three most commonly available pneumatic motors are the axial piston, radial piston, and _____.

5. Motors which are designed to operate in only one direction are called _____.

6. Smoother rotation is obtained from a vane type motor with more _____.

SEGMENT 3

PNEUMATIC SCHEMATICS

OBJECTIVE 9	DESCRIBE THE LINE SYMBOLS USED WITH FLUID POWER CIRCUITS

Up to this point, this learning system has discussed a number of pneumatic schematic symbols and covered some basic schematics. However, knowing how the symbols for the conductors are shown is a necessity to have before properly drawing the circuits. Each type of line or conductor is shown in figure 32.

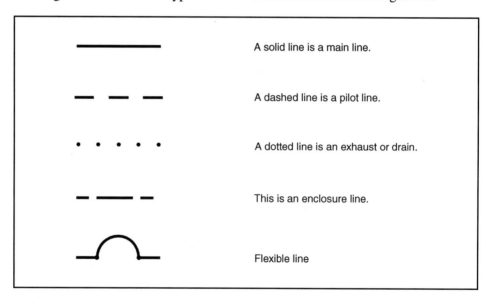

Figure 32. Line Symbols Used in Fluid Power

Procedure Overview

In this procedure, you will be given several pneumatic symbols, which you have seen previously, and asked to match them with their description.

❑ 1. Identify and match each symbol with its description. This will help you in learning the schematic symbols used in pneumatics.

A.　　　　　　　　　＿＿＿＿＿＿　AA.　Bidirectional Pneumatic Motor

B.　　　　　　　　　＿＿＿＿＿＿　BB.　Lever Operator

C.　　　　　　　　　＿＿＿＿＿＿　CC.　Tee

D.　　　　　　　　　＿＿＿＿＿＿　DD.　Enclosure Line

E.　　　　　　　　　＿＿＿＿＿＿　EE.　Muffler

F.　　　　　　　　　＿＿＿＿＿＿　FF.　Double-Acting Cylinder

G.　　　　　　　　　＿＿＿＿＿＿　GG.　Blocked Line

H.　　　　　　　　　＿＿＿＿＿＿　HH.　Spring

I.　　　　　　　　　＿＿＿＿＿＿　II.　Flow Direction

J.  _____ JJ. 2-Way, DCV, N.O.

K. _____ KK. Single-Acting Cylinder

L. _ _ _ _ _ _____ LL. Exhaust Line

M. _____ MM. Main Conductor

N. _____ NN. Regulator

O. _____ OO. 3-Way DCV, N.C.

P. _____ PP. Quick-Connect

Q. · · · · · · · · _____ QQ. Pressure Gauge

R. _____ RR. Hose

S. _____ SS. 3/2 DCV, N.O.

T. _____ TT. Filter

U. _____ UU. Shutoff Valve

V. _____ VV. Unidirectional Pneumatic Motor

W.   _____ WW. Cross

X. _____ XX. Pilot Line

Y. _____ YY. 5/3 DCV, Manually-Operated

Z. _____ ZZ. 2/2 DCV, N.C.

OBJECTIVE 10	DESCRIBE SEVEN BASIC RULES FOR DRAWING PNEUMATIC SCHEMATICS

There are seven rules to follow when drawing pneumatic schematics:

1. **Symbols may be rotated or reversed without altering their meaning.**

   An exception is with conditioning components equipped with drains (filter, lubricators, etc.) These are usually shown with the drain port down, as shown in figure 33.

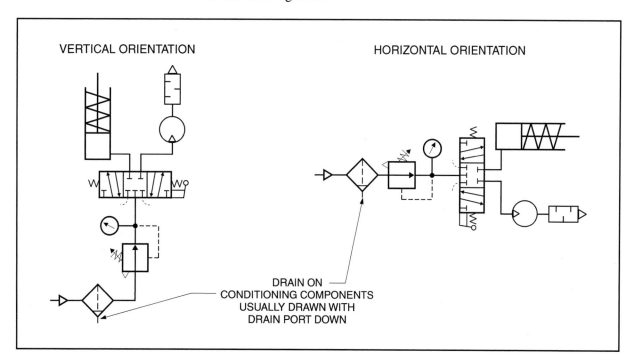

Figure 33. Two Versions of the Same Schematic

2. **Lines (conductors) are shown either horizontally or vertically on the schematic diagram. Diagonal lines should not be drawn.**

3. **Connecting lines, crossing lines, and blocked lines should be drawn, as shown in figure 34.**

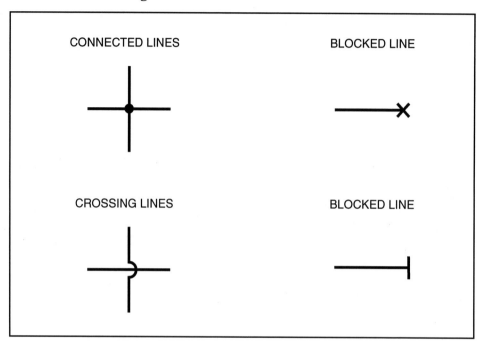

Figure 34. Line Connections

4. **Symbols show connections, flow paths, and functions only.**

   They do not show construction, size, location of ports, flow rate, or pressures.

5. **Each symbol is drawn to show normal, at rest, de-energized, or neutral condition of the component.**

   The only exception is when multiple diagrams are drawn showing various phases of circuit operation.

6. **Letters may be used as part of graphic symbols but are not necessary except M inside a circle to denote an electric drive motor.**

7. **A hollow arrow (open triangle), as shown in figure 35, indicates a flow of air from the air compressor. This can be used by itself to represent the air supply from the air compressor or a partial section of a circuit.**

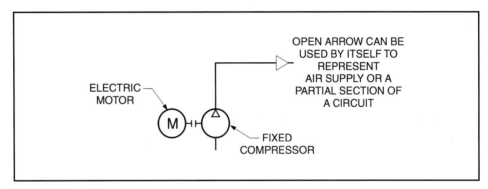

Figure 35. Schematic of a Partial Pneumatic Circuit

Procedure Overview

In this procedure, you will draw schematics by looking at actual circuit connections on pictorials. This is a common requirement in industry because the schematics are not often readily available.

❑ 1. Draw the circuit schematic on a copy of figure 37 for the pictorial shown in figure 36. Start from the supply manifold as shown. You may show flexible tubing as a rigid connector (i.e. a straight line) and leave out all quick-connect symbols.

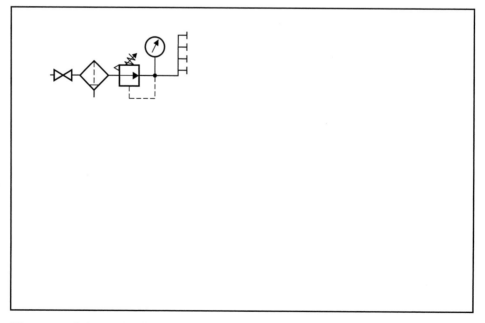

Figure 36. Pictorial of a Basic Pneumatic Cylinder Circuit

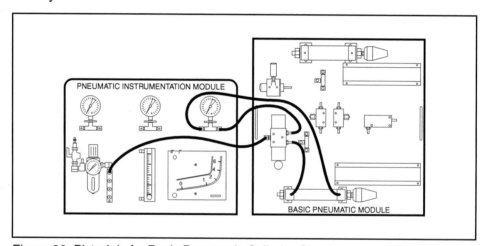

Figure 37. Schematic of a Basic Pneumatic Cylinder Circuit

❏ 2. Draw the circuit schematic on a copy of figure 39 for the pictorial shown in figure 38. Start from the supply manifold. You may show flexible tubing as a rigid connector (i.e. a straight line) and leave out all quick-connect symbols.

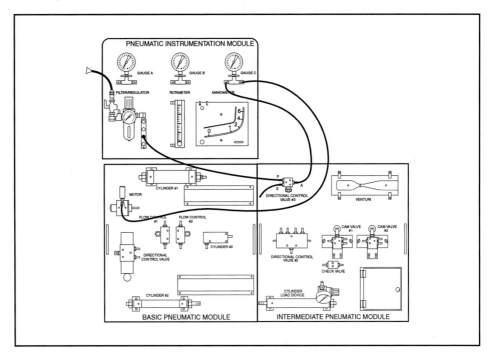

Figure 38. Pictorial of a Basic Pneumatic Motor Circuit

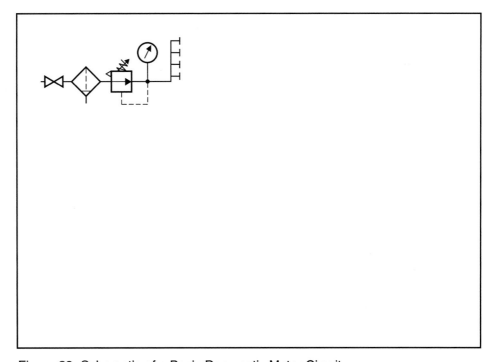

Figure 39. Schematic of a Basic Pneumatic Motor Circuit

❑ 3. Draw the circuit schematic on a copy of figure 41 for the pictorial shown in figure 40. Start from the supply manifold. You may show flexible tubing as a rigid connector (i.e. a straight line) and leave out all quick-connect symbols.

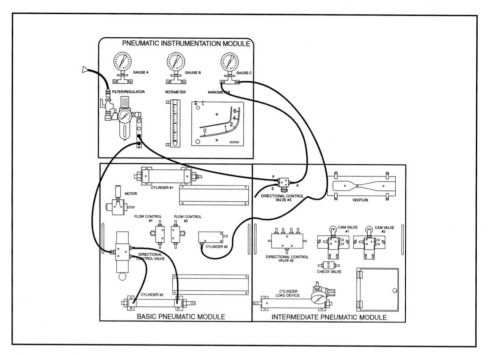

Figure 40. Pictorial of a Pneumatic Circuit

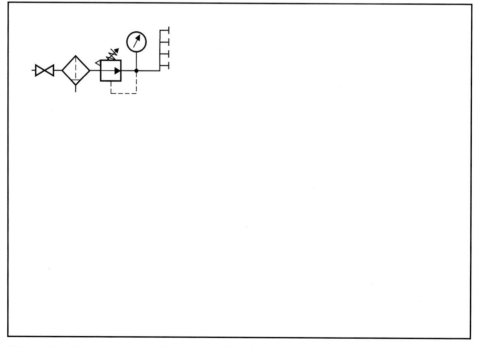

Figure 41. Schematic of a Pneumatic Circuit

Procedure Overview

In this procedure, you will draw on a pictorial of the pneumatic trainer the actual circuit connections given a schematic. This will help you develop your skills in reading schematics.

❑ 1. Draw the circuit hose connections between circuit components on a copy of the pictorial shown in figure 43 given the schematic of figure 42.

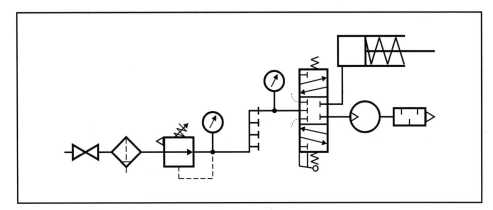

Figure 42. Schematic of a Pneumatic Power Circuit

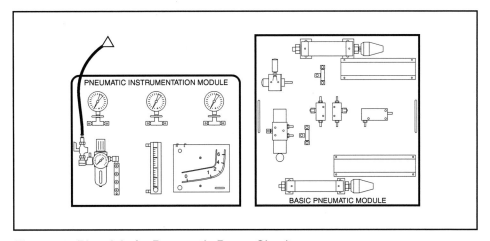

Figure 43. Pictorial of a Pneumatic Power Circuit

❑ 2. Draw the circuit hose connections between circuit components on a copy of the pictorial shown in figure 45 given the schematic of figure 44.

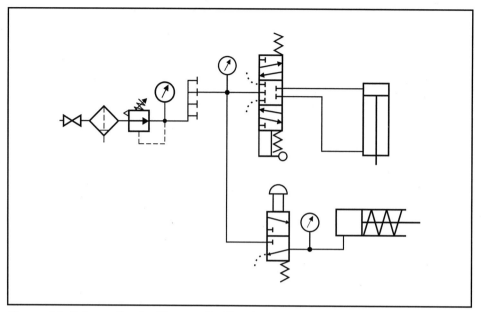

Figure 44. Schematic of a Pneumatic Circuit

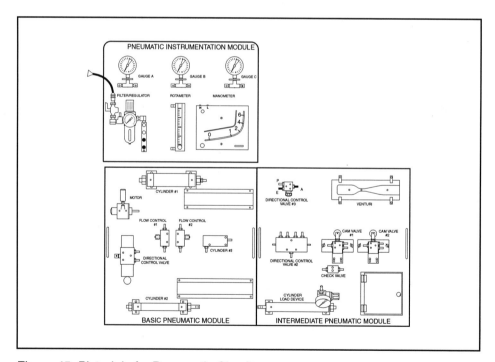

Figure 45. Pictorial of a Pneumatic Circuit

❑ 3. Draw the circuit hose connections between circuit components on a copy of the pictorial shown in figure 47 given the schematic of figure 46.

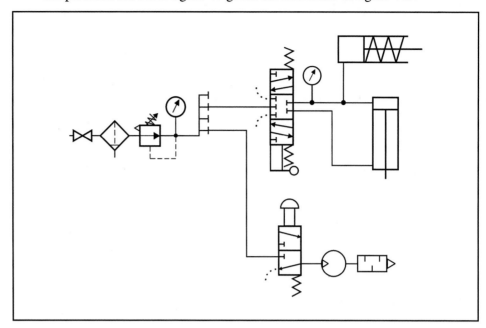

Figure 46. Air Flow From the Compressor

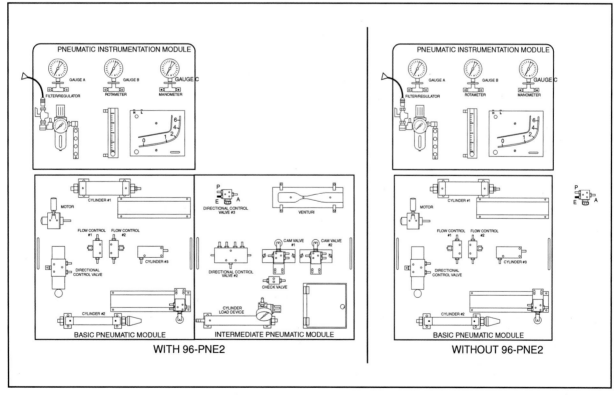

Figure 47. Air Flow From the Compressor

Procedure Overview

Now that you have learned how to draw schematics, you will get a chance to combine this skill with your creativity to design a more complex pneumatic circuit.

☐ 1. Read the following scenario.

Scenario: You have been assigned to design a pneumatic circuit to operate the automated drill machine shown in figure 48. Provide the following operations:

- Clamp cylinder opens and closes to clamp parts in position.
- An eject cylinder extends and retracts to remove parts from the drill station.
- A drill cylinder extends and retracts to drill the parts.

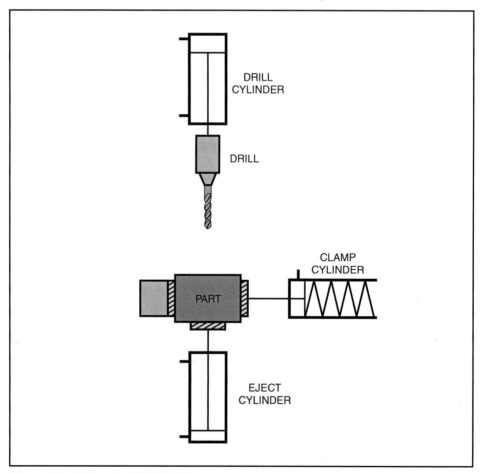

Figure 48. Automated Drill Station

Each cylinder should be separately controlled by its own DCV. Use lever-operated DCVs.

Notice that the clamp cylinder is a single-acting, spring-extend type. The reason for this is so the part will stay clamped (cylinder extended) if pneumatic power is lost. If you used a double-acting cylinder, it could lose its clamping power while the drill is drilling. When you design circuits, you should always look at the operation of the design during emergency states as well as normal states.

Design the drill cylinder circuit so the drill automatically retracts if you release the lever of the DCV.

❑ 2. Draw the circuit schematic that will perform the operations described in step 1. Start with the air supply line shown in figure 49. Add a filter and regulator.

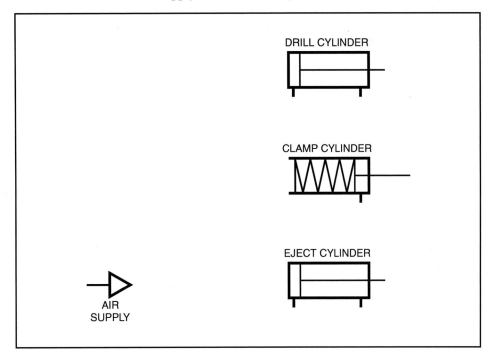

Figure 49. Circuit Schematic

1. A dotted line represents a(n) _____, when using pneumatic schematics.

2. The letter M inside of a circle indicates _____.

3. Dashed lines indicate a(n) _____ line when using pneumatic schematics.

4. Symbols may be _____ or _____ without altering their function or condition.

5. A hollow arrow in a schematic indicates that the medium is _____.